Mission 4:
Too Close to the Sun

by Andy Russell

Illustrated by Mike Perkins

CHAPTER ONE

The Mission Control radio burst into life.
All spaceships in this corner of the Solar
System were listening.

This is the Argosy 9211, on our way to Solar Station Three. Engines have failed! Life support is failing! We are drifting towards the sun. Send help, please! We are carrying an important cargo that must be saved!

My brother Ben and I were on our way home. We had just dropped some tourists at Luna Base. We needed a rest, not an adventure.

Our sleek new ship, a Pulsar-9, was one
of the fastest on the market. We had been
saving all our credits for over a year to buy
it. How could we ignore the message?

We didn't know it then, but on the other side of the sun was an even faster ship. Inside was a crew of mean and ugly pirates. They had heard the message too, and they were also heading for the Argosy.

CHAPTER TWO

Moments later, Ben and I were on our way to the last known position of the Argosy.

"Can't you make this go any faster?" I asked.

"We are at top speed already," replied Ben. "Any faster and we'll blow the engines. You leave the flying to me and get on the radio. See if they can hear us."

"I've tried. There's no answer," I said.

"Have a look on the long range scanner. We should be able to see them soon." said Ben.

I switched on the scanner. It wasn't long before a small blue dot appeared. It was on the far side of the screen.

"At this speed, we will be with them in an hour," I said. "Hey, what's that?"

Another dot showed on the screen. It was heading straight for the stranded Argosy.

"The scanner says it's an Astro 4. Isn't that the ship those pirates used?" I asked.

"Yes," said Ben, "but it's not just pirates who fly them. It could be anybody. And anyway, those pirates should still be locked up. Try calling them up."

I tried the radio. There was no reply, and still nothing from the Argosy. As we got closer to the sun, the radio was full of static.

"If it is pirates," said Ben, "why do you think they are interested in this important cargo?"

"Maybe it's loads of gold," I said. "Perhaps they'll give us a big reward and we could buy an even better ship."

"I wonder if they've seen us?" said Ben

We were soon to find out ...

CHAPTER THREE

"I can see the Argosy through the window," I yelled.

I was in my T-shirt. The sweat was dripping off me from the heat. The huge orange ball of the sun filled the whole view. The stranded Argosy was just a speck in the distance.

"We'll be docking in two minutes,"
said Ben. "Better get suited up."

Just as he spoke, a loud alarm began to
sound.

"Warning!" said the voice of the
computer. "Radiation alert! Temperature
alert! Twelve minutes to overload!"

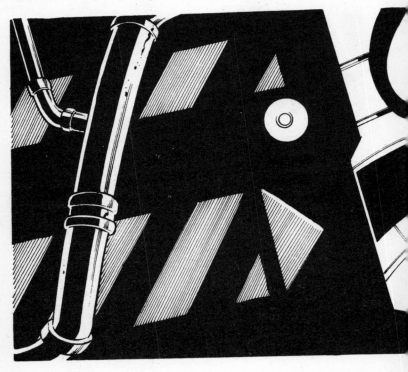

"Twelve minutes, Ben!" I said. "Can we do this in time?"

"No problem," said Ben. "We'll be out in ten minutes."

"What happens if we overload?"

"Don't ask," said Ben.

Moments later, we landed with a loud thud on the hull of the Argosy. The captain, Sharon Peters, and her crew were lying on the floor. The heat had made them collapse. The air was thin, it was an effort to breathe.

As we opened the airlock, they all staggered to their feet. It took a great effort, but they managed to get their suits on.

Luckily, we had not suffered from the heat so much. We were able to drag all the crew into our ship. In the background the computer said, "Warning! Four minutes to overload."

"Quick, Ben," I said, "get the engines going."

A small voice croaked, "Don't forget the plans!" It was Sharon.

"What plans?" I asked.

"It's our important cargo," said Sharon. "They are for a new kind of space engine. You mustn't let them burn."

"Leave them!" ordered Ben.

"You can't," croaked Sharon. "They're just inside the hatch, in a locker."

"I'll be two minutes," I said as I went through the hatch. "Don't go without me!"

I pulled myself into the Argosy. Bits of plastic were melting off the walls. Where were the plans?

I saw the lockers along one wall. I checked the first – no plans. In the second was a steel tube. Inside was a box containing a computer disk. The box was already starting to melt from the heat.

As quickly as I could, I pulled myself back to the hatch. I leapt through it and slammed the heavy door.

"Warning! Thirty seconds to overload!" said the computer.

"Go, Ben!" I yelled as I slammed into my seat.

With only seconds to spare the ship pulled away from the Argosy. Ben quickly turned it so the hot side faced away from the sun. We all waited. Would the alarm stop? A minute went by but the computer was silent. Then the alarm stopped.

Sharon and her crew cheered. "Well done lads!"

CHAPTER FOUR

But we had no time to celebrate. First we
had to help the crew. They were in a bad
way. Their skin was burnt and their
clothes all torn. They'd had a very
narrow escape.

When the crew were sorted out, I looked at the scanner. "That Astro is catching us up," I said to Ben. "There is still no answer on the radio."

"I'm sure it's the pirates," said Ben. "If they are gaining on us, what can we do?"

"They must be after the plans," croaked Sharon. "You must not let the pirates get them. If they do, they could capture any ship in the galaxy."

"Don't worry, they won't beat us," I said.

"They know we are slower. They know we have the plans. We can't outrun them so what can we do?" asked Ben.

"Change course, Ben. Steer the ship straight past the pirates towards the sun."

"You must be crazy!" said Ben.

"Trust me," I said, as I pulled my spacesuit back on.

"Now what are you doing, Sam?"
asked Ben with a horrified look on his face.

"I'm just taking a spacewalk, Ben," I
said. "You just fly the ship. I'll be back
soon."

CHAPTER FIVE

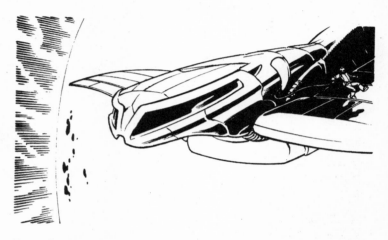

I picked up my tool belt and stepped into the airlock. Then the outer hatch opened and I was outside. I carefully pulled myself along the ship. I was heading for the cargo hold, near the back.

Being close to the sun, I had to be careful to stay in the shade. I would fry if I didn't.

I reached the cargo hold. I took a spanner and carefully began to remove the bolts holding the radiation shields in place. My plan was to take them from the empty cargo hold and put them over the crew section. With the radiation shields to protect us, we would be safe.

I tried to ignore the sweat dripping down my face. This would be a hot job.

Minutes later, I glanced up as we passed the pirate ship. Sure enough it began to turn. My plan was working – they were following us!

CHAPTER SIX

After what seemed like hours, I came back in through the airlock.

"Well done, Sam," said Sharon. "Let's hope it works."

The Pulsar went on, straight towards the sun. All around the crew section were the radiation shields that I had moved. My plan was working – so far. The heat was not too bad and no alarms had sounded.

"The Astro is still gaining on us," I said. "It's less than an hour away."

"In less than an hour we will all be dead from the radiation anyway, if your plan doesn't work," said Ben.

"It will work," I said. "It's got to."

The air in the Pulsar was starting to get much hotter now. The water supply was almost gone. The radiation levels were creeping up towards the red. It wouldn't be long before the alarms went off.

Sharon was looking out of a window. "I can see them!" she called.

Everyone went to look out. The Astro was clearly visible in the distance. We could see that it was getting closer as we watched.

"Come on, Ben, we've got to find somewhere to hide those plans before they get here," I said.

"How can they last this long so close to the sun?" Ben asked.

"I don't know," I replied, "but we have to hope that we can last longer than them."

CHAPTER SEVEN

Everyone on board the Pulsar, except Ben, was still looking out of the window. Ben was studying the control panel carefully.

The radiation warning was just on the red section. Any minute now and the alarms would sound. We would have to turn back and face the pirates.

"What's that?" called Sharon. "I
thought I saw something near the pirate
ship."

"Yes, I saw it too," I said. "It looked
like an escape pod to me. Ben, can you get
anything on the sensors?"

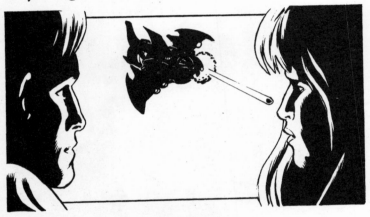

"I'll have a look," said Ben.

He bent over the sensor panel just as
the radiation alarm began its warning.
The computer joined in. "Warning,
Warning! Radiation alert! Radiation alert!
Twelve minutes to overload."

"Sam," called Ben. "The scanners are picking up an escape pod with life forms in it."

"They must have abandoned ship!" said Sharon. "And look at the Astro."

She pointed through the window. The Astro was glowing, first with a green colour, then through orange to red, then white. Suddenly there was a bright flash and the Astro was gone.

The pirates in the escape pod could do nothing but drift through space, until they were picked up by the Galactic Police.

Everyone cheered! We had beaten the pirates. Ben turned the Pulsar round and set a course for Earth. The escape pod with the pirates on board drifted past the window. It would be a long time before they caused trouble again!